Earth Science Series

WATERS OF THE EARTH

written by Virginia Powers Leftwich
illustrated by Larry Weaver

CONTENTS

Indicates full color transparency.

*Page 1 — CHEMICAL PROPERTIES OF WATER

CONCEPT: Water plays a very important part in the chemistry of the earth.

Water is composed of two parts of hydrogen and one part oxygen. **Electrolysis,** the passage of an electric current through water, provides proof of the composition of water. The most widely used electrolysis device is the Hoffman apparatus. The electrodes are glass insulated electrical leads terminated with a piece of platinum. The stopcocks open to allow the apparatus to be filled with a solution of water and electrolytic solute. The electrolyte is necessary for the conduction of the electric current. The stopcocks are then closed so the gas will not escape. The hydrogen collects at the **cathode** (the negatively charged electrode) and oxygen collects at the **anode** (positively charged electrode), in the whole number ratio of 2:1.

Water is an oxide of hydrogen and has the polar covalent bond. The molecule is nonlinear. There is an angle of 104.5° between the two hydrogens. The two projecting hydrogens are positively charged and the oxygen atom is negatively charged. The shape of the molecule allows the charge to be polarized. Water molecules are dipoles. Water may be characterized as a polar solvent.

The polarized nature of the water molecule makes it readily active in hydrate crystal growth. It is an active agent for dissociating ionic crystalline substances. In the reaction of crystalline table salt (NaCl) with water, sodium and chlorine are ionized and the water dipoles surround these ions, pulling them into solution away from the crystalline lattice. The positive sodium ion is thus surrounded by water dipoles with the negative pole directed toward the chlorine ion. Because the electrical force of the water dipoles is greater than the electrical attraction of the two ions in the crystal, the crystal dissociates (dissolves).

Crystalline materials which incorporate the H_2O molecules into the crystal structure are called **hydrates**. Crystalline copper sulfate is a blue hydrate containing five molecules of water for each copper sulfate molecule. If the crystals are heated gently, the water is driven off and the copper sulfate loses its blue color and becomes white or grayish. When water is allowed to return, copper sulfate hydrate is reformed. The reaction is

$$CuSO_4 + 5H_2O \rightarrow CuSO_4 \cdot 5H_2O$$

Water is indispensable. Because it so readily combines with so many elements and compounds, it is known as the universal solvent. Its role in photosynthesis makes life on earth possible. Its role as a dissociating agent makes the oceans saline. Its role as a hydrate helps to shape some of the crystalline crust of the earth.

FURTHER STUDY: 1. Find out about the different kinds of heavy water and the role of heavy water as a possible energy source. 2. What theories are used to explain the manner in which green plants are able to decompose water during photosynthesis?

ACTIVITIES: Construct models of water, hydrates, chloride ions, etc.

*Page 2 — PHYSICAL PROPERTIES OF WATER

CONCEPT: Because of the uniqueness of the behavior of the water molecule, we use the water molecule as a standard for the quantative physical descriptions of other solutions.

Pure water is odorless, colorless, and tasteless. The odor or taste typically associated with water is due to dissolved material in it. While water is colorless, large bodies of it transmit enough short wave light to give it a pale blue appearance. Pure water freezes at 0° C and boils at 100° C. Water is the basis of standards for physical descriptions of other substances. The weight of one milliliter of water taken at 4° C is one **gram**, the unit of weight in the gram weight system. The weight to volume ratio of water taken at 4° C is the standard for judging density. If the mass of 1 centimeter ^{3} of a substance is less than one gram, then its density is less than 1. If the mass of 1 centimeter ^{3} of a substance is greater than 1 gram, then the density will be expressed in numbers greater than 1. The number that indicates the weight of a substance compared with the weight of an equal volume of water is called the **specific gravity** of the substance.

The freezing point and the boiling point of water are used as the **calibration indices** for thermometers. The Fahrenheit scale marks these two indices as 32° and 212°. The Celsius scale marks them as 0° and 100°.

The heat capacity of water is used as the standard for both the calorie and the B.T.U. (British Thermal Unit). A **calorie** is defined as the amount of heat needed to raise 1 gram of water 1^OC from 14.5^OC to 15.5^OC. The **B.T.U.** is defined as the amount of heat needed to raise one pound of water 1^OF from 63^OF to 64^OF.

At the boiling point and the freezing point, a considerable amount of **latent heat** is needed to change the physical state of water. Eighty-four calories, the **heat of fusion**, are necessary to change one gram of ice at 0° C to 1 gram of water at 0° C. The same amount of heat must be removed from 1 gram of water at 0° C to convert it into 1 gram of ice at 0° C. The **heat of vaporization** is the five hundred forty calories needed to convert 1 gram of water at 100° C to 1 gram of steam at 100° C. The **latent heat of condensation** released when 1 gram of steam condenses to liquid is also 540 calories.

The density of water increases until it reaches 4^OC. Below this point the density drops until it becomes ice at 0° and has a density of 10/11 of the density of water at 4° C. The significance of this is that ice floats. When water is cooled to 4° C it sinks.

Polarity makes it possible for the water molecule to form hydrogen bonds with other molecules having unpaired electrons. These bonds are the result of electrostatic forces made possible by the strength of the water dipole. Four electrostatic bonds per water molecule are possible. The maximum number of electrostatic bonds are formed in crystalline water (ice). Each water molecule occupies a fixed position. The fixed position of each water molecule forces the molecules to occupy a volume approximately 1/9 greater than that needed for noncrystalline water. Gaseous water (steam) has no electrostatic bonds, and liquid water which may have any number from zero to four, has a mean number of two. The electrostatic bonding in liquid water is restrictive only at the surface. Otherwise, the water molecule cluster may slip (pour) over other molecule clusters. The molecules at the air-water interface are subjected to a different situation. There are no water molecules on top to slip over; the direction of the electrostatic bonding becomes quite specific. The surface molecules in water thus form a relatively tough film described as **surface tension**. The cohesiveness of electrostatic surface bonding produces a minimum surface area which causes the water drop to be spherical. The cohesive force is sufficient to support relatively dense objects if they have a large surface area and resist wetting. The floating razor blade or needle demonstrate the force of the surface tension of water. This surface tension is weakened by adding a wetting substance such as soap.

The phenomenon called **capillarity** is the consequence of the cohesiveness of water and the formation of hydrogen bonds between the water and the surface molecules of the ascent material. Capillarity will not occur with materials incapable of forming hydrogen bonds. The extent to which water rises in a capillary channel is a function also of the diameter of the channel. The rise is greatest in the channel with the smallest bore and least in the channel with the largest bore.

Page 2A — Experiment

Results and answers are dependent upon the temperature to which the water samples are to be heated. Experimentation should be followed by analytical and speculative discussion.

*Page 3 — DISTRIBUTION OF THE EARTH'S WATER

CONCEPT: Because water is unevenly distributed throughout the world, there are varying types of living conditions and, therefore, varying types of **flora** and **fauna**.

Hydrologists have estimated that the accessible water on earth is in excess of 326 million cubic miles. This amounts to about 0.024% of the earth's mass.

The oceans contain an estimated 317 million cubic miles, or 97.2% of the total supply of earth's water. All of the oceanic water is sufficiently saline to form a restrictive biological environment and a very corrosive physical environment. Approximately 0.026% of the water of the ocean is evaporated annually.

The glaciers and icecaps hold the second largest percentage of the earth's water. The amount of water in the solid state varies from age to age. At present, glaciers and icecaps contain about 7 million cubic miles or 2.15% of the total accessible water.

The mean volume of water in the atmosphere is estimated to be about 3,100 cubic miles. An estimated 93,000 cubic miles of gaseous water evaporates from the oceans each year. Most of this evaporated ocean water condenses and falls back into the ocean. The atmospheric water is changed on an average of every two weeks.

Approximately 2 million cubic miles of water is present in the earth's crust in a form that could be claimed. This is only about 0.625% of the total supply. This small percentage of water includes the most significant of the earth's waters—soil moisture. Statistically, soil moisture amounts to only 16 thousand cubic miles of water, 0.005% of the total earth supply, but it is this water that supports plant and animal life. Various methods of irrigation have been devised in an attempt to increase the amount of usable soil moisture. Most of the crustal water that has been economically recovered for this purpose, has been from within the first one half mile of the crust. This water is stored in **aquifers** (porous materials). The economically recoverable ground water found within the top one half mile, represents 0.31% of the earth's supply and is estimated to be 1 million cubic miles. The problems related to the recovery of ground water are extremely complex. The extent of aquifers below the half mile point is not well known. This 1 million cubic miles of water is too expensive to harvest. Ground water may require 10,000 years to complete a cycle.

Large lakes, inland seas, and rivers collectively contain only 55,300 cubic miles of water, 0.017% of the earth's supply. More than half of this surface water, (30,000 cubic miles) is stored in fresh water lakes; 25,000 cubic miles is stored in inland seas and salt lakes which are too saline to be useful agriculturally. The rivers and streams contain only one percent as much water found in the fresh water lakes. The running surface water is estimated to be 300 cubic miles of water, about 0.0001% of the world's supply.

FURTHER STUDY: 1. Find out how water and its management has affected the development and endurance of early civilizations of the world. 2. What is the North American Water and Power Alliance?

Page 3A — Graphing the Distribution of Earth's Water

Completed graphs will vary according to the categories of water which individual students choose to consolidate. Any system which a student can logically defend is acceptable.

CONCEPT: Three basic aspects of the water cycle (evaporation, precipitation, and runoff), provide the earth with the steady source of fresh water necessary to sustain life, and are the major forces in changing the surface features of the earth.

An estimated 93,000 cubic miles of water are evaporated annually. Approximately four fifths of the water vapor comes from the oceans. The balance is a combination of evaporation from inland water bodies, and evapotranspiration from the land plants and animals. On a percentage basis, the evaporative forces are considerably more effective over the land mass than over the ocean. With approximately 97% of the available water only 4/5 of the vapor comes from the oceans, while the land mass (glaciers contain an additional 2%) with less than 1% of the available water, contributes 1/5 of the water vapor. The basic difference relates to the higher temperatures reached on the land, and the fact that a larger percentage of inland water is exposed to air. Inland water bodies are shallow while oceans are deep and, therefore, only a small percentage of ocean water is exposed to evaporative forces.

Water condenses around fine particles in the atmosphere. The condensation action is directly observable in cloud forming, in fog, and in the formation of frost and dew. Condensation alone is significant in supplying large quantities of water to shore areas, but on a global basis, the condensation process is significant only as a precursor to the precipitation process.

The precipitation aspect of the hydrologic cycle is the main mode of interaction between the atmosphere and lithosphere. There are three major patterns of precipitation—orographic, cyclonic, and convectional. The orographic pattern is significant where the moisture-laden prevailing winds encounter mountain ranges. The air is forced to rise over the barrier. In the process of rising, condensation and precipitation deliver most of the precipitative moisture on the windward side of the mountain. The leeward side is usually left dry and is called a rain shadow. The cyclonic or air mass pattern is significant in the temperate latitudes as a mechanism for precipitation during the winter season. Lifting is produced by the collision between contrasting air masses. The convectional thunderstorm is caused by uneven heating and the consequent development of strong thermal updrafts. The convectional pattern is significant world-wide. There are an estimated 4 million thunderstorms annually—an average of about one thunderstorm every eight seconds.

Precipitation frequently is evaporated on its way to the ground. This forms the null cycle. Seventy-five percent of the precipitation that falls to the earth, falls over the oceans. This precipitation forms what is called the short cycle. The balance, an estimated 24 thousand cubic miles of water, falls on the land and becomes a part of the long cycle of the hydrologic cycle. The long cycle provides the means by which the lithosphere interacts with the hydrosphere and the atmosphere. In areas where there is extensive vegetation, between 5-15% of the precipitation is intercepted and evaporatranspired without having touched the ground. The precipitation that strikes the ground is partly absorbed by the soil in the infiltration process. The extent of infiltration depends on the slope of the ground, porosity of the soil, level of saturation, and the rate of precipitation. About 10% of the precipitation becomes ground water. If the water table is normal, ground water will seep or run by springs into the surface channels so that it is eventually returned to the ocean. Considerably more time is required for the ground water to make its way back to the ocean. About 72% of the precipitation evaporates from the inland water bodies, from the soil, or from the living things through evapotranspiration.

FURTHER STUDY: 1. What attempts have been made to produce rain artificially? What were the results? 2. What attempts have been made to reduce evapotranspiration?

Page 4A — Developing a Hydrologic Cycle

Students should not be encouraged to duplicate the hydrologic cycle shown on page 4. Any representation which shows the relationship of precipitation to evaporation as well as the importance of runoff is acceptable.

*Page 5 — WATER BUDGETING

CONCEPT: The local water budget is a record and interpretation of the average amount of source water, its storage, and use.

A local water budget is similar in many respects to a family money budget. The budget covers a year and is typically arranged to allow for a monthly audit. The monthly water income from the water cycle is based on mean figures representing several years of record keeping of precipitation amounts. The expected income is dependent upon the precipitation (P). The expected outgo, potential evapotranspiration (PE), is the evapotranspiration that would occur if there were a continuous source of moisture. The difference between precipitation and evapotranspiration (P — PE) is recorded in black if the water from precipitation is sufficient to supply the water that is evapotranspired. If the potential evapotranspiration exceeds the precipitation, the difference is recorded in red.

The amount of water that is added to or subtracted from the soil moisture is recorded as the change in soil moisture (ΔST) for a given month. The balance is recorded as the amount of stored soil moisture actually present at the end of the month (ST).

Soil water is increased only when the amount of rain is greater than the amount of evapotranspiration. The actual amount of water experiencing evapotranspiration cannot exceed the total amount of water available from precipitation and from the soil. Therefore, a separate column is used to record the actual water lost through actual evapotranspiration (AE). AE is either equal to or less than P — PE.

The amount of water that can be stored in the soil is finite. The field capacity depends on the depth and the character of the soil, but is generally considered to be between 4 and 6 inches of water. The standard water budget assumes a maximum storage capacity of 100 mm (about 4 inches). The water budget expresses the quantities of water in terms of millimeters, rather than in inches, because the smaller unit makes it possible to deal with whole numbers. When actual evapotranspiration is greater than the combined amounts of precipitation and actual evapotranspiration, a deficit will occur. On the other hand if the soil is at full-field capacity and the precipitation level exceeds the evapotranspiration level there will be a surplus and runoff will occur.

FURTHER STUDY: 1. Research the data of real field capacity in your area. Make and compare two water budgets for your area, one using the real field capacity and the other using 100 mm as the field capacity. 2. Construct some daily water budgets for your area.

ACTIVITY: Students determine when irrigation should begin.

Page 5A — Calculating the Water Budget
Page 5B — Local Water Budget (Tucson, Arizona)

LOCAL WATER BUDGET												

TUCSON, ARIZONA WATER BUDGET water measured in millimeters												
	JAN.	FEB.	MAR.	APR.	MAY	JUNE	JULY	AUG.	SEPT.	OCT.	NOV.	DEC.	TOTAL
P	21	22	19	10	5	7	56	55	29	14	20	25	283
PE	16	21	37	65	114	170	192	176	142	79	32	16	1060
P-PE	5	1	-18	-55	-109	-163	-136	-121	-113	-65	-12	9	
ΔST	5	1	15	0	0	0	0	0	0	0	0	9	
ST	14	15	0	0	0	0	0	0	0	0	0	9	
AE	16	21	34	10	5	7	56	55	29	14	20	16	
DEFICIT	0	0	-3	-55	-109	-163	-136	-121	-113	-65	-12	0	
SURPLUS	5	0	0	0	0	0	0	0	0	0	0	9	

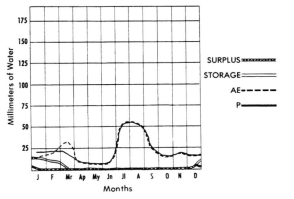

Before students attempt to figure either of the water budgets, they should fully understand each entry in the St. Louis water budget.

Page 5C — Local Water Budget (New Orleans, Louisiana)

LOCAL WATER BUDGET												

NEW ORLEANS, LOUISIANA WATER BUDGET water measured in millimeters												
	JAN.	FEB.	MAR.	APR.	MAY	JUNE	JULY	AUG.	SEPT.	OCT.	NOV.	DEC.	TOTAL
P	127	133	142	134	119	115	136	106	73	85	111	152	1433
PE	15	18	45	75	122	164	179	170	129	69	31	15	1032
P-PE	112	115	97	59	-3	-49	-43	-64	-56	16	80	137	—
ΔST	0	0	0	0	3	49	43	5	0	16	80	4	—
ST	100	100	100	100	97	48	5	0	0	16	96	100	—
AE	15	18	45	75	122	164	179	111	73	69	31	15	—
DEFICIT	0	0	0	0	0	0	0	-59	-56	0	0	0	—
SURPLUS	112	115	97	59	0	0	0	0	0	0	0	133	—

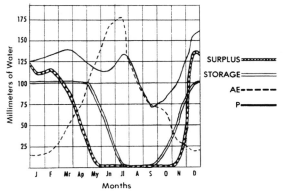

*Page 6 — SUBSURFACE WATER

CONCEPT: Subsurface water is the major reservoir of liquid fresh water and the cycling of it is the most significant circuit of the hydrologic cycle.

An estimated 2 million cubic miles of water lie in the underground **aquifers** (porous rock that may hold water). This represents about 97% of the earth's supply of liquid fresh water. Most of it is no more than two miles deep. Half of it is within one-half mile of the surface.

About one tenth of the land precipitation becomes subsurface water. Subsurface water includes the **capillary water** of the soil and the unbound **gravity water** of the bedrock and overburden. Capillary and gravity water make up about .625% of the earth's water. They hold the greater part of the liquid fresh water. **Soil water** is the most important aspect of the subsurface water because of its role in supporting plant growth. **Ground water** is a main source of usable water.

Subsurface water is classified as meteoric, magmatic, or connate. Most of the subsurface water is **meteoric**—derived from the infiltration and percolated precipitation aspects of the hydrologic cycle. Part of the water escaping during volcanic activity may be **magmatic**—vaporized from molten rock. **Connate** water is water trapped in the pores of sedimentary rocks at the time it was laid down. Connate water does not naturally circulate as does meteoric water.

Meteoric water enters the soil through cracks (if the soil is very dry) or through **pores**. The size of the pores determines the rate at which water infiltrates the soil. Some of the infiltrating water becomes bound to the soil particles by capillary attraction. The amount of capillary water the soil can hold depends on the extent of the soils capillary space. Fine grain soil, such as clay, at full-field capacity, hold more capillary water than do coarse grain, sandy soils at full-field capacity.

Water in the soil in excess of the full-field capacity becomes gravity water and **percolates** downward into the **rock fracture zone,** underlying the soil.

Meteoric water flows through two major zones, the zone of aeration, and the zone of saturation. The **zone of aeration** is filled with gravity water and is usually delineated from below by an impervious rock layer. Percolation direction is generally vertical or slightly oblique in the zone of aeration. While the water movement in the **zone of saturation** is generally lateral, it may be in sweeping arcs.

The zone of aeration is subdivided into three regions: the **soil water region** the **intermediate region,** and the **capillary fringe region.** Evapotranspiration processes can remove the capillary water in the soil water region but not from the intermediate belt. The capillary fringe lies at the interface between the zone of aeration and the zone of saturation. The capillary fringe might be thought to represent the top of the water table, but the level of the water in a well stays below the level of the capillary fringe. The water of the capillary fringe is, as the name implies, capillary rather than gravity water. The depth of any of the regions of the zone of aeration may vary. The depth of the soil water region, usually rather constant for an area, is determined by the depth of the weathered and organic material present. The depth of the intermediate zone will change with the rise and fall of the level of saturation or the level of the water table. A seasonal fluctuation in the water table is to be expected in areas where serious deficiencies in the water budget occur at a certain time of the year.

The zone of saturation is established when the percolating water encounters a layer which is relatively impermeable, the **aquiclude** or aquitard. As the percolating water reaches the level of the aquiclude, it begins to back up until all the pore space of the permeable layer is filled. The top of the zone of saturation is called the **water table. Head** describes the level of the aquiclude to which there is pressure enough to raise the water if a fracture should occur.

Since the water in the zone of saturation is gravity water, this aquifer layer will yield water. Water may escape from the aquifer as springs or seeps. A **spring** is defined as an issue of water sufficient to create a distinct stream or current. A **seep** is characterized by a slow escape not characterized by or evidencing a distinct flow. In areas of contrasting relief, the springs may appear high on a hillside. The water table that feeds such springs is called a **perched water table.** It is perched in that it is geographically isolated from the main aquifer. The water table of the main quifer in humid areas is usually very near or slightly above the surface level of the major streams or rivers that drain the surface water. Swamps and marshes represent areas in which the water table coincides with the surface of the land or lies a short distance below it. Water from the main aquifer in humid areas seeps into the stream, providing water for runoff during the season of reduced precipitation and increased evapotranspiration. Channels supplied by ground water are called **effluent streams.** The water table typically drops during any extended period in which recharge from gravity water does not equal or exceed the water lost through seepage or spring flow.

In arid areas the main aquifer usually lies below the major drainage channel. In this case, the water seeps from the overlying stream into the aquifer. The amount of seepage reduces the stream flow until the stream may eventually cease to flow. Channels of this sort are called **influent streams.**

Artificial wells may be sunk below the level of the water table of the aquifer. Water thus collects in the well cavity by gravity flow from the surrounding saturated material. The productivity of a well is judged by the rate at which water flows into the cavity. The rate of flow may vary from 2 gallons per minute in fine grain aquifers to several thousand gallons per minute in coarse grain alluvial aquifers. Occasionally the geology of an area will have tilted the aquifer so that the recharge area is at a much higher elevation than the ground level of areas sinking wells into the aquifer. When this happens the water is under such hydrostatic pressure that it will rise to the level of the water table forming an **artesian well.** (On the transparency, discuss what would happen if the water table (and water head) were raised. What would cause the water table and water head to be raised?)

Hot springs occur where parts of an aquifer lie on or near hot magma from the mantle area. Springs flowing from such aquifers emit heated water, usually laden with the minerals characteristic of the aquifer material. Geothermal heat from the magma is also responsible for the vertical emission of steam-water in **geysers.** A geyser differs from a spring in that the water from a geyser is ejected in an erratic and explosive manner at a considerable distance above the aquifer rather than on the level of the aquifer. The ground water collects in channels connected to the hot magma. The water adjacent to the magma becomes super heated, changes to steam, and forcefully expels the overlying water as increased pressure forces it to expand.

Water from the fresh water aquifers along coastal areas seep into the ocean rather than into rivers and streams. Fresh water is lighter than salt water, so that the water table of the aquifer will be above, rather than level with, the mean ocean level. A problem has developed regarding the pumping of water from shoreline aquifers. When water is removed faster than the aquifer can be recharged, salt water seeps inland. This is called **overdrafting.**

FURTHER STUDY: 1. How can aquifers be artificially recharged? 2. How does the chemical character of underground water usually differ from surface water?

*Page 7 — RIVERS AND STREAMS

CONCEPT: Streams and rivers carry the surplus water from the land to the oceans and are the principal cause of change in surface features of the earth.

Earth's rivers and streams contain an estimated 300 cubic miles of water which represents only one millionth of the total supply, only 1/7000 of the liquid freshwater, only .54% of the liquid surface water. The small percent of the earth's water in the rivers and streams has proven to be adequate for man's personal needs and adequate as a source of food supplement through the life that it supports.

Rivers and streams exist where the processes of evapotranspiration and subsurface seepage cannot progress rapidly enough to handle the meteoric water of the moment, and where the rate of seepage from the ground water exceeds the evapotranspiration rate. The surplus water from these sources returns to the oceans by these surface channels.

The path the runoff follows is called a **channel.** The initial channels are usually determined by geological irregularities in the landscape. The water flows into and along these low areas, grading them as it does so by dissolving matter and by erosion. The land sculpturing action of flowing water may alter the landscape so that the final drainage pattern bears no resemblance to the initial channels. The sculpturing action eventually defines a drainage basin which is outlined by a drainage divide. A **drainage divide** either directs water into or away from a particular drainage basin. Large, well-established basins become known as **watersheds.**

Drainage channels typically become larger as the water progresses downstream to sea level. An American engineer, Robert Horton, used the order of interceptions of channels to describe a particular drainage source. A drainage channel with no tributaries is classified as a **1st order stream.** A channel with one or more 1st order tributaries forms a **2nd order stream;** a channel with one or more 2nd order tributaries is a **3rd order stream,** etc. Such an approach to stream classification has produced some interesting regularities. The higher the order of a stream, the greater its length and the greater the area of its watershed. There are generally three or four tributaries of the next lower order.

In hilly regions the streams of the same order generally run parallel to each other and have tributaries which intercept them at nearly right angles. A system of this sort is called a **trellis pattern.** In smooth, gently sloping areas the streams of the same order are obliquely orientated toward each other and have tributaries which intercept them at angles other than 90°. A system of this sort which resembles the branching in a tree root is called a **dendritic pattern.** These are the two most common stream patterns.

Based on the flow pattern of a stream, there are three main types: permanent, intermittent, and interrupted. A **permanent stream** acts as a drainage channel for runoff meteoric water as well as a drainage source for ground water overflowing the main aquifer. Permanent streams have two flow levels, a high level when surface water is being drained, and a low level designed to handle only the ground water. **Intermittent streams** carry primarily surface runoff. There are seasonal dry periods. If there is ground water feeding an intermittent stream, it is insufficient to overcome loss during evapotranspiration. **Interrupted streams** are characterized by interrupted surface and subsurface flow. Such streams may flow in underground channels for several miles before resurfacing.

Stream channels are typically sculptured over long intervals of time to provide for the efficient disposal of the average annual surface runoff. During a normal year the channel proves adequate to contain the stream. Each stream has its own characteristic flow pattern, but there are some irregularities of flow that are almost characteristic of temperate latitude streams of the humid areas. The average stream will fill level with its banks no more than twice a year. This **bankfull** stage is most common in the spring when the greatest water budget surpluses occur. The average stream will overflow its banks and slightly inundate its own flood plain, forming what is called a **natural levee.** On the average of once every 10 years, the stream will overflow its banks and the natural levee. At intervals of, perhaps, 20 to 100 years, there will be a major flood during which the river will inundate the terraces which are part of the flood plain.

FURTHER STUDY: 1. What are some of the major problems in the construction of dams on major rivers? 2. What are some of the interpersonal, intercommunity, interstate, and international disputes, that have developed over the use of water from streams and rivers. 3. What are the characteristics of anastomatic and radial stream patterns?

Page 7A — Mapping Stream Order

Students should understand that, for this project, researching the seemingly insignificant lower order streams of one major river, is more important than showing all of the major rivers of North America. Large atlases or road maps from gasoline stations will provide the necessary details.

*Page 8 — LAKES—STANDING WATER

CONCEPT: A lake is a body of water that has been temporarily delayed in its cycle back to the oceans.

Fresh water lakes contain an estimated 30,000 cubic miles of water. This represents only 0.009% of the total world supply, but it is 100 times more water than is contained in the rivers and streams. Salt lakes and inland arms of the sea hold 25,000 cubic miles of water. The total amount of standing water is 0.017% of the total water of the earth.

While rivers and streams grow continuously, lakes shrink continuously in size. While rivers represent natural avenues designed for the efficient return of surplus water to the ocean, lakes are geologic irregularities which cause delays in the return to the ocean. Lakes in humid areas generally have a water outlet, but in arid regions evaporation may cause a lake to be saline or even to dry up entirely.

Several geologic processes can create lakes. Basins formed by movement of the earth's crust are **tectonic lakes**. Lake Okeechobee in Florida and Reelfoot Lake in Tennessee are tectonic lakes. Most of the lakes of North American were formed by glacial action through scouring or damming of drainage channels with glacial deposits. The Great Lakes and the Finger Lakes are **glacial lakes**. Small **sinkhole** lakes are formed by solution processes. Solution lakes are formed in areas where there is extensive limestone strata located in the water table. Solution processes along fractures and fission lines create large caverns which eventually collapse. Solution lakes in sinkholes are widespread in Florida, Kentucky, and Indiana. Rivers may act to produce lakes. The **oxbow lake** is a characteristic feature of meandering rivers in mature flood plains. Landslides may also form dams and, in turn, lakes.

The depth and surface area of a lake is the result of the process that formed the lake. Deep lakes are not necessarily lakes with large surface areas. The deepest American lake is the volcanic crater lake which is about a mile deep. It does not compare in surface area to the Great Lakes. The deepest known lake is the tectonic Russian Lake Baikal which is over a mile deep. Lake Baikal is only slightly larger in surface area than Lake Erie.

The chronological age of a lake is generally calculated by counting varves. A **varve** consists of a coarse layer of sediment which is formed in the spring, and a fine layer formed in the winter. There are two major types of lakes. A new, clean bottom lake with little or no biological community is called an **oligotrophic lake**. Oligotrophic lakes are usually both geologically and biologically young. A shallow lake with extensive sediment, a high concentration of biological constituents and a high level or organic production is called a **eutrophic lake**. Eutrophic lakes are usually both geologically and biologically old. The marsh stage usually follows the eutropic stage. **Marshes** are broad wet areas supporting grasses and sedges and are characterized by frequent small patches of shallow bare water. The **swamp** stage follows the marsh stage. Swamps are wet low lands which support woody stemmed plants and have only a small percentage of bare water. The swamp stage gives way to a **wet terrestrial community** as production and sedimentation build to elevate the surface level slightly above the water table.

Although lakes are bodies of standing water, there is some circulation of the water. Lakes are subject to waves caused by the wind. Larger lakes have a periodic oscillation in the basin called a **seiche**. The temperate latitude lake of mean depth also manifests another type of seasonal circulation and stratification which helps to improve the efficiency of the biological nutrient cycle. This circulation is brought about by the density differences in water of varying temperature. Following the spring thaw of ice, the lake experiences a thorough mixing of the water from top to bottom. This mixing serves to lift dissolved minerals to the surface layer.

The diagram shows the stratification of a typical north temperate lake. By June or July, the **epilimnion**, the oxygen rich upper zone, contains the warmest water in the lake and circulates freely. There is a regular small decline in the water temperature with increasing depth. The middle zone, the **thermocline**, shows drastic declining of temperature and oxygen. This decline in temperature continues with depth down to the bottom layer, the **hypolimnion**. The hypolimnion is a uniform $4^{\circ}C$ and is oxygen poor. This thermal stratification prevents a mixing of the water of the lake.

With approaching autumn this stratification deteriorates. The temperature differences between the water of the epilimnion and the thermocline become less. The epilimnion encroaches on the thermocline. When the waters of the lake have reached a uniform 4° C, there is again mixing throughout. During the winter freeze, the coldest water is no longer on the bottom, but it is the ice that floats on the surface. The ice prevents circulation and the lake becomes stagnant. The spring thaw brings the lake to 4° C again.

Circulation is not characteristic of tropical lakes. Perhaps this is one reason why tropical lakes are not, as a rule, as biologically productive as temperate latitude lakes which are deep enough to experience seasonal thermal stratification.

FURTHER STUDY: 1. What is the controversy regarding the extent to which man is accelerating the eutrophication process in Lake Erie. Discuss proposed solutions to the dilemma. 2. What is the ecological value of ponds created by beaver damming.

Page 8A — Lake Succession

Student drawing and lists will vary.

*Page 9 — GLACIERS AND ICECAPS

CONCEPT: Temperature and altitude cause much of the earth's supply of fresh water to be temporarily stored in the solid state in icecaps and glaciers.

The single largest supply of the world's fresh water is in the glaciers and icecaps. An estimated 7 million cubic miles of water, 2.15% of the earth's total water supply, and 77.37% of the earth's supply of fresh water is stored as ice at altitudes and latitudes where temperatures and water budget surpluses make this possible. There is some solid fresh water on every continent except Australia. The largest existing glacier covers Antarctica with a layer of ice averaging 2 miles thick.

The geologic record indicates that the relative proportion of the water of the hydrologic cycle that joins or departs from the glaciers and icecaps is subject to considerable variation over rather long intervals of time. The fluctuations are due to warming and cooling periods of the earth. The current hydrologic cycle reflects the level of glacial growth and decay during what is believed to be a warming period. A cooling period would produce glacial advances and bring about an **ice age**. Continental glaciation is the consequence of lowering the temperature and increasing the snowfall at a time when evaporation is static or reduced. The appearance of an ice age is related to a set of complex factors which cause intervals between glaciations.

There is evidence for a glacial period in the Paleozoic Era, and one in Cambrian time. The better documented glacial period involving North America occurred during the Pleistocene Epoch. Four glacial stages are generally recognized. The glacial flows came from three accumulation centers: the Labrador center in southeastern Canada, Keewatin center in central Canada, and the Cordilleran center in the Canadian Rockies. The centers were not always equally active and the four glaciations involved some overlap of region. Each glacial stage except the first does have distinctive end moraines.

The earliest Pleistocene glaciation, the **Nebraskan glacial stage**, extended south to the Missouri River in Missouri, into Southern Illinois, west to mid-eastern Nebraska, northward through the Dakotas, and east to the St. Lawrence River area. The southwestern part of the **Kansan glacier** is well defined, but the southeastern portion was subsequently reglaciated. The third glaciation, the **Illinoian glacial stage**, extended the farthest south of any glacier. It extended to what is currently the Ohio River. The Illinois glacier created the Ohio River by blocking and diverting the flow of the enormous Teays River away from its Illinois river drainage. The Illinois glacier remained east of the Mississippi River until it was deep in Minnesota. It then dipped southwestward into Iowa and northwesterly through the Dakotas. The eastern extension slightly overrode the Kansan. It terminated in the lower St. Lawrence River valley. The fourth and last glaciation, the **Wisconsin glacial stage**, developed considerably less southern thrust than the prior glaciers, but it extended eastward to Long Island.

The flowing behavior of icecaps and glaciers is related to the physical behavior of the hexagonal snow crystal. Snow crystals become granular snow when compressed. Granular snow compacts to a stage called **firn**. Pressures at a depth of 200 feet or more changes firn into a brittle glacial ice. Pressure from above causes the bottom layer to break down the crystalline structure and become supercooled water. This supercooled water behaves like a viscous liquid, lubricating the mass and allowing it to flow. The supercooled water can be recrystallized when the pressure changes. This makes it possible for ice to flow around immovable objects. The Wisconsin glacier flowed around a highland called Driftless Area, south of Lake Superior. Glaciers flow more rapidly near their centers than along the flanks, and the top flows faster than the bottom. Normally, glaciers flow less than one foot per day. Valley glaciers have been known to flow as fast as three feet per day. Fractures called **crevasses** usually appear at a transverse angle to the glacial arm. **Meltwater** flows down through the crevasses, underneath the ice, and emerges at the ice front. The milky appearance of this water is related to the suspended rock dust load that the meltwater carries. The outflow deposits some of the suspended material in an outwash plain before it flows to the ocean.

FURTHER STUDY: 1. What are some of the proposals regarding ways to avert a new ice age. 2. What impact do some scientists feel pollution will have on the glacial cycle?

Page 9A — Mapping of Glaciers and Icecaps

Student maps will vary depending upon research sources. The fourth center is Greenland.

CONCEPT: The oceans and seas contain a high percentage of the earth's water, are the major contributor of gaseous water, and the major vehicle for the transfer of solar heat.

An estimated 97.2% of the world's water is stored in the oceans and seas. All of the 317 million cubic miles of ocean water is saline. The percentage ratio of the various salts is uniform. The seven most prevalent salts and their relative percentages of concentration are listed below.

> sodium chloride 77.8%
> magnesium chloride 10.9%
> magnesium sulphate 4.7%
> calcium sulphate 3.6%
> potassium sulphate 2.5%
> calcium carbonate 0.3%
> magnesium bromide 0.2%

Three ions account for 94% of the weight of the salt content in ocean water: chlorine 55%, sodium 31%, and sulphate 8%. A small percentage of metal ions are present in sea water. While the ratio of salts to each other is constant, the percentage of salinity is not uniform throughout the oceans. Salt concentration ranges from 3.3% to 3.7%. This concentration difference is, for the most part, related to uneven distribution of evaporation and precipitation. The most evaporation and the least precipitation occur between 20° and 30° of latitude. Since salts are left behind when water evaporates, this region is the zone of maximum salinity. The zones of minimum salinity are the equatorial area where there is extensive rainfall, and the polar areas where evaporation is slight and the melt from ice supplies large quantities of fresh water.

The differences in the level of salinity, difference in temperature, wind action, gravitational action from the moon and sun, and the earth's revolution cause waves, currents, and tides. Waves increase the surface area of the ocean and facilitate evaporation. Waves also cause some mixing. Currents are significant in the transfer of heat and have a marked effect on world climates. Currents also deliver oxygenated water to great depths and make possible the deep sea forms of life which live below the photic zone (zone penetrated by light). Tides are significant erosive forces.

There are surface features on the ocean floor: mid-ocean ridges, underwater valleys and canyons, plateaus, and deep trenches. The average depth of the ocean is 2-1/2 miles. The depth of the ocean varies from sea level, along the shores, to between six and seven miles, in the deepest trenches.

The variation in the water level caused by the tides creates an intertidal zone. The open water of the oceans form the pelagic zone. The continental shelf is an area of the continent that is covered by the ocean. The continental shelf, usually found on eastern coasts, slopes away from the shoreline for an average distance of 100 miles. The water over the continental shelf has an average depth of 200 feet and forms what is called the neritic pelagic zone. The ocean floor along the continental shelf is usually covered with sediments from the continent. The shallow continental shelf sediment is called the littoral benthic zone. Here, biological activity is high because of the availability of mineral nutrients and efficient mixing. A sharp dropoff called the continental slope marks the edge of the continental shelf. The bottom of the continental slope and the bottom of the abyssal plain form the deep-sea benthic zone. The deep water overlying the slope and the abyssal area constitutes the oceanic pelagic zone. Areas of the ocean where the water is very deep are usually fairly unproductive because there is not enough mixing between the top and the bottom to provide the needed nutrients. There may be productive areas where there is sufficient upwelling and overturn to provide a continuous supply of mineral nutrients needed for plant growth.

FURTHER STUDY: 1. What are the problems related to any effort to farm the ocean bottom. 2. What was the result of the deep sea exploration done by the bathyscaphe Trieste?

Page 10A — Mapping the Ocean Floors

Students will need to research atlases and geographic magazines for these maps. Student maps will vary according to research sources.

*Page 11 — ANCIENT INLAND SEAS OF NORTH AMERICA

CONCEPT: Mountain building, geosyncline sedimentation, and the extensive periods of glaciation determine which areas of the continents are inundated or dry.

At the beginning of the Paleozoic Era, two oceanic arms invaded the North American Continent along major north-south orientated coastal geosynclines. These inland seas made islands of the high lands: Appalachia and Acadia in the Atlantic, and Cascadia in the Pacific. The climatic conditions of this time are believed to have been such as to foster rapid erosion of the highlands so that the seas should have been excluded by sedimentation of the geosyncline basins. The geologic processes at work during this time continued with the uplifting of the high areas so that the sedimentation could not keep pace with the sinking of the geosynclines. Oceans invaded. Late in the Cambrian Period an additional geosyncline, the Ouachita, developed across the south central portion of what is now the United States, permitting the invasion of an arm of the ocean into the continental interior. Two additional islands were created by this ocean, Llanoria, and Mexicoia.

The Paleozoic inland seas reached the peak of invasion during the Ordovician Period. At this time, the warm shallow inland seas covered 60% of the continental land mass. These seas receded throughout the remainder of the Paleozoic Era. The minimum invasion of the Paleozoic Era occurred during the Permian Period, about 270 million years ago. The events of the Permian Period which produced this retreat of inland seas are believed to have completed the Appalachian and Ouachita Mountains. The sedimentation of the geosynclines related to these mountain chains, and the general lowering of the ocean level as a consequence of the reported extensive glaciation of the Permian Period. The Cascadia uplift had not been completed, and the geosyncline did not fill sufficiently to exclude the inland sea from the Cordilleran geosyncline.

The Eastern, Central, and Northern portions of the North American Continent remained generally free from oceanic invasions throughout most of the Mesozoic Era. The inland sea of the Cordilleran or Rocky Mountain geosyncline continued to come and go throughout the Triassic and Jurassic Periods. The maximum size of the inland sea of the Rocky Mountain geosyncline was reached in the late Cretaceous Period, about 70 million years ago. The Rocky Mountains matured during the Cretaceous. The Rocky Mountain geosyncline was at its maximum depth at that time. The inland sea extended all the way from the Gulf of Mexico to the Arctic Ocean east of the Sierra Nevada Mountains and Rocky Mountains. The erosion of the Ouachita Mountains of the south, and the reduction of the Appalachian Mountains to hills during the late Cretaceous caused a sinking of the Gulf Coastal Plains, allowing an inland advance of the Gulf of Mexico up the Mississippi River to about the present junction with the Ohio River and from there across the southern portion of the southern states. The Mesozoic Era ended with a two island continent divided by an inland sea.

There was no further major mountain building of the Cenozoic Era but the Cascadian Revolution did occur during this time, and the Wasatch Mountains were formed by faulting. In general the Cenozoic era was one of sedimentation. The North American continent began to take on a modern look. By the beginning of the Miocene Epoch about 25 million years ago, the Rocky Mountain geosyncline had filled again. The only inland sea remaining by Miocene time was the Gulf of California. The extent of the oceanic invasion of the continental land mass involved the inundation of the still emerging Gulf Coastal Plains, the Atlantic Coastal Plains and the California Coastal Plains. Sedimentation and coastal plain emergence finally excluded the ocean from these coastal areas and restricted the Gulf of California by the middle of the Pliocene Epoch about 4 million years ago. The North American shoreline appeared very much as it does now. The Pleistocene Epoch produced four glaciations which affected the level of the ocean. The drop in the level of the ocean allowed a land mass extension along the continental shelf area and was most extensive in the Gulf of Mexico area. Following the glaciations the oceanic basins returned generally to their Pliocene limits.

FURTHER STUDY: Find out if the other continents were invaded by inland seas and if so, if the invasions occurred at the same time invasions were taking place in the North American Continent.

ACTIVITY: If there are fossiliferous marine rock outcrops in your area, visit them and collect some of the fossils. What do the fossils tell you about the nature of the sea?

Page 11A — Mapping Ancient Inland Seas of North America — I

Page 11B — Mapping Ancient Inland Seas of North America—II

Students will need to research in geology textbooks, etc. in order to complete these maps. Student maps will vary according to research sources.

*Page 12 — POWER FROM WATER

CONCEPT: The force of moving water is a large natural concentration of energy— the only known usable source of the energy generated by gravity.

The first device designed to make use of the energy of moving water is believed to have been developed in the first century B.C. A wheel with projecting paddles was laid on its side at the edge of a swift moving stream. The force of the current against the paddles caused the wheel to rotate. A vertical shaft was attached to a grinding stone which rotated as the wheel was turned. Later, the Romans developed an upright wheel with a horizontal shaft attached to a grinding stone. Gears multiplied the speed of the rotation of the grinding stone. Modifications made it possible for the water wheel to operate a variety of pieces of equipment in which a rotating motion could be used. Channeling the water into a sluice upstream from the water wheel, causing it to fall on the wheel, increased the distance of fall of the water and the amount of energy available.

At the beginning of the 20th century, falling water was used to generate electrical energy. The generator had to be turned at a very high speed. The falling water was made to strike the vanes of a water turbine. The rotation of the water turbine powered the generator. Dams were constructed to maximize the distance the water fell, concentrating the potential energy of the water. The water from the dam was delivered to the water turbine by means of long tubes called **penstocks**. The water under great force was directed against the vanes of the turbine rotor at the proper angle to produce the greatest impact. The high impact energy turned the turbine rotor at a very rapid rate.

The gravity relationship of the earth-moon-sun system is the energy source of tidal power. The force of the incoming tide is kinetic energy, and the back and downward flow of the returning water is the same as the potential energy of falling water. Tidal power was first used for the generation of electricity in 1966. A dam was built across la Rance estuary in France. The facility uses advanced design horizontal axial flow turbines. Adjustable blades generate electricity by using the kinetic energy of the incoming tide as well as the potential energy of the return fall of the high tide water stored behind the dam.

Only a few sites exist where tidal conditions are such that tidal power can be utilized with the present level of mechanical efficiency. At present, there must be a regular high tide and a basin geologically suitable to store the high tide water. Present estimates of the potential of tidal power place it as only 1% of the total power needs of the world.

FURTHER STUDY: 1. Find out what kind of conditions determine the location of a favorable dam site for the generation of electricity. 2. Find out where the highest tides of the world occur and try to figure out why the tides are highest at these sites.

ACTIVITIES: 1. Visit a dam. 2. Build working models of the first two water wheels shown. How do the gears affect the speed of the movable grindstone? 3. Build a model dam. Using a water wheel, compare the power above the dam and below it.

Pages 13-16 — UNIT TEST ON WATERS OF THE EARTH

Some questions in this test assume that the student has completed the suggested readings from the Student References listed at the end of this guide.

1. B	11. D	21. D	31. A	41. D
2. C	12. B	22. D	32. B	42. A
3. A	13. B	23. A	33. C	43. C
4. C	14. A	24. C	34. B	44. B
5. B	15. C	25. C	35. B	45. D
6. B	16. B	26. B	36. A	46. A
7. A	17. D	27. A	37. C	47. B
8. D	18. B	28. D	38. C	48. B
9. A	19. D	29. C	39. A	49. B
10. C	20. B	30. D	40. D	50. A

GEOLOGICAL SURVEY REGIONAL OFFICES

Atlantic Coast Region — The States of Connecticut, Delaware, Florida, Georgia, Maine, Maryland, Massachusetts, New Hampshire, New Jersey, New York, North Carolina, Pennsylvania, Rhode Island, South Carolina, Vermont, Virginia, West Virginia, the District of Columbia, the Commonwealth of Puerto Rico, and the Virgin Islands.

Regional Hydrologist, WRD . . . . Phone [202] 343-8841
Atlantic Coast Region
George Washington Building
Arlington Towers
1011 Arlington Blvd.
Arlington, Virginia 22209

Rocky Mountain Region — The States of Arizona, Colorado, Kansas, Montana, Nebraska, New Mexico, North Dakota, South Dakota, Texas, Utah, and Wyoming.

Regional Hydrologist, WRD . . . . .Phone [303] 233-3611, ext. 6701
Rocky Mountain Region
Building 25
Denver Federal Center
Denver, Colorado 80225

Mid-Continent Region — The States of Alabama, Arkansas, Illinois, Indiana, Iowa, Kentucky, Louisiana, Michigan, Minnesota, Mississippi, Missouri, Ohio, Tennessee, and Wisconsin.

Regional Hydrologist, WRD . . . . Phone [314] 268-7224
Mid-Continent Region
2222 Schuetz Rd., Suite 212
St. Louis, Missouri 63141

Pacific Coast Region — The States of Alaska, California, Hawaii, Idaho, Nevada, Oregon, and Washington.

Regional Hydrologist, WRD . . . . Phone [415] 325-6761, ext 337
Pacific Coast Region
345 Middlefield Road
Menlo Park, California 94025

Your Geological Survey Regional Office will direct you to your state Geological Survey Office. Your State Geological Survey Office will be most helpful in directing you to current government documents and other aids to you in presenting this unit.

RESOURCES

Battan, Louis J., *The Nature of Violent Storms*, Doubleday & Co., Inc., Garden City, New York, 1961.

Bauer Helen, *Water: Riches or Ruin*, Doubleday & Co., Inc., Garden City, New York, 1959.

Carson Rachel L., *The Sea Around Us*, Oxford University Press, Inc., New York, 1961.

Cocannouer, Joseph, *Water and the Cycle of Life*, The Devin-Adair Co., New York, 1958.

Engel, Leonard, *The Sea*, Time Inc., New York, 1961.

Harris, Miles F., *Man Against the Storm: The Challenge of Weather*, Coward-McCann, Inc., New York, 1962.

Lehr, Paul E., R. Will Burnett, and Herbert S. Zim, *Weather: A Guide to Phenomena and Forecasts*, Golden Press, Inc., New York, 1957.

Leopold, Luna B., Kenneth S. Davis, and the editors of *Life, Water*, Time Inc., New York, 1966.

Thompson, Phillip D., Robert O'Brien and the editors of *Life, Weather*, Time Inc., New York, 1965.

Contact the nearest Geological Survey Office. They will be able to supply you with an up to date and appropriate list of government publications and other helps.

Name _____ Date _____

EXPERIMENT

ACTIVITY: comparing the relationship between time and temperature when the amount of water to be heated is changed

PROCEDURE: Apply a steady heat supply to water samples of 50 ml and 100 ml. Take the temperature of the samples at regular intervals. Record your readings:

Time											
Temp. 50 ml											
100 ml											

Graph your readings:

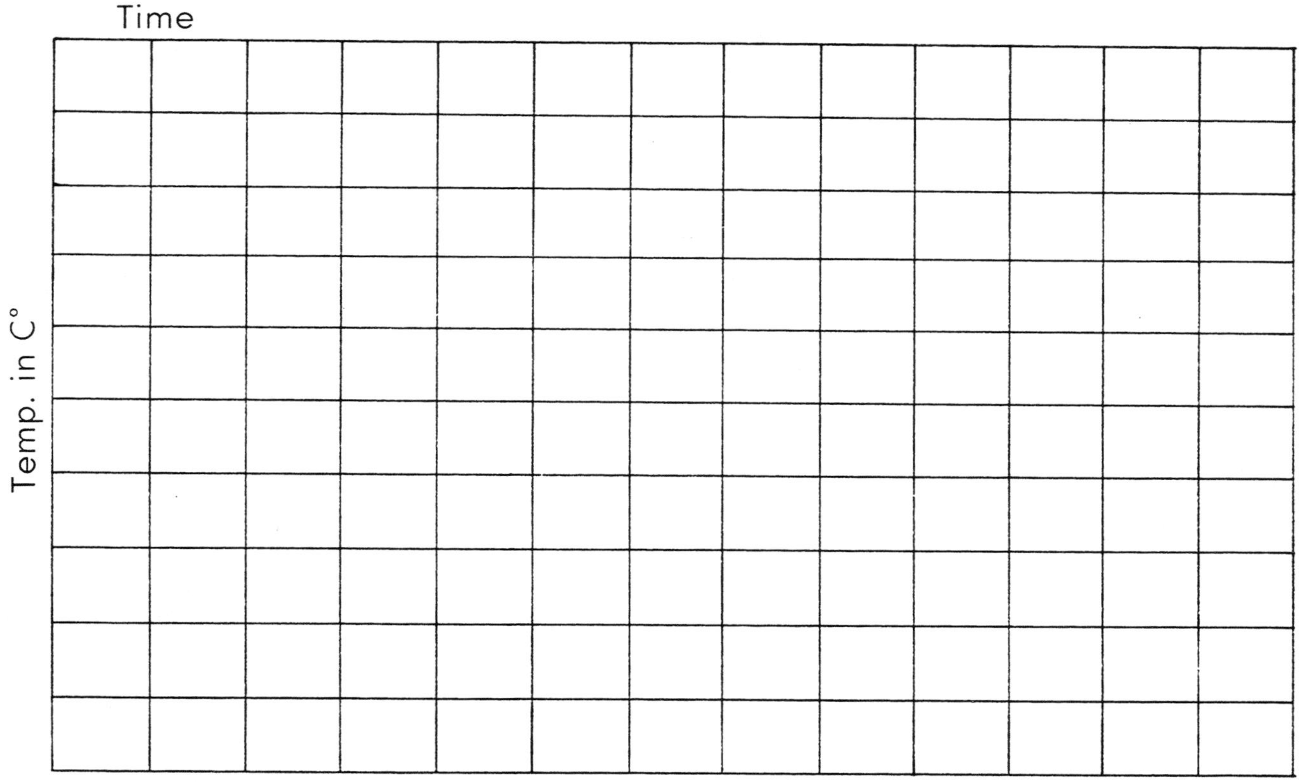

Time

(blank graph grid — Temp. in C° on vertical axis)

Does a 100 ml sample of water require twice as much heat as the 50 ml sample to raise its temperature to the same degree?_____ Explain. _____

Does a 100 ml sample of water require twice as much heat as the 50 ml sample to raise its temperature to the same degree? _____ Predict the line on your graph for a 200 ml sample. Test for your prediction. Was your prediction correct? _____

Suggest a method for measuring heat based on this activity: _____

_____

_____

Name _____ Date _____

GRAPHING THE DISTRIBUTION OF EARTH'S WATER

Using the percentages on the right, devise a workable method of graphing the percentage distribution of the earth's water on the circle graph and on the bar graph. Which one do you find easier to read? _____

Why? _____

Would a line graph be appropriate?
_____

Explain: _____

Fresh-water lakes 0.009%
Saline lakes and inland seas . . . 0.008%
Rivers 0.0001%
Soil moisture 0.005%
Ground water 0.61%
Icecaps and glaciers 2.15%
Atmosphere 0.001%
World oceans 97.2%

Source

%

MILLIKEN PUBLISHING CO.

Name _____ Date _____

DEVELOPING A HYDROLOGIC CYCLE

Sketch in the space below your interpretation of the hydrologic cycle. Show the happening in as much or as little detail as you think will tell the whole story. Simplicity and clarity are as important as completeness.

4A

MILLIKEN PUBLISHING CO.

CALCULATING THE WATER BUDGET

The first step in the calculation of the water budget is to determine wetting and drying periods by calculating P—PE for each month. When P—PE is positive, it indicates a wetting period; when it is negative, it indicates a drying period. This is entered in the third line of the table.

The fourth and fifth lines in the table, Δ ST and ST, are used to account for the moisture in the soil. Line four, Δ ST is the amount of change in soil moisture storage for the month. Line five (ST) is the amount remaining in storage at the end of the month.

ST can be negative, positive, or zero. If P—PE is negative, moisture is being withdrawn from storage during a drying season. ST is then negative, and its amount is subtracted from the ST brought forward from the previous month. When all the moisture storage is withdrawn, ST will be zero until the first wetting month. During a wetting season (P—PE positive), ST will be positive, adding to the storage account until the 100 mm capacity is reached. Then it will be zero until the first drying month. Even though a surplus of moisture is available, the soil is unable to accept any more.

This limit in storage capacity enables you to find a starting point. If for any series of months, the P—PE values are positive and when added together total more than 100 mm, you know that at the end of that series of months, the ST brought forward is 100 mm.

Once you have established a starting point, proceed to calculate AE, D, and S. Three cases need to be considered: (1) a drying month, (2) a wetting month, and (3) a neutral month (AE=PE).

1. In a drying month, less moisture is supplied by precipitation than the amount that could be evaporated and transpired. Consequently moisture must be withdrawn from storage to make AE equal to PE. When the storage is reduced to zero, any further demand causes a water deficit, D. In this event, AE will equal P, which is less than PE. The amount of the deficit will be the difference between PE and AE.

2. In a wetting month, more moisture is supplied than can be evaporated or transpired. This excess is put into storage. When the amount in storage reaches 100 mm, the maximum amount the soil can hold, any remaining moisture is considered surplus, S. Water surplus penetrates to the ground-water table or is lost as surface runoff. It cannot be used by plants. When P is greater than PE, AE always equals PE.

3. In a neutral month, all the precipitation is used, with none left over. AE equals PE and Δ ST is zero. ST remains unchanged.

ST is the only value carried forward from month to month. All other values depend only on the P and PE values for each month.

LOCAL WATER BUDGET

TUCSON, ARIZONA WATER BUDGET
water measured in millimeters

	JAN.	FEB.	MAR.	APR.	MAY	JUNE	JULY	AUG.	SEPT.	OCT.	NOV.	DEC.	TOTAL
P	21	22	19	10	5	7	56	55	29	14	20	25	283
PE	16	21	37	65	114	170	192	176	142	79	32	16	1060
P-PE	5										-12	9	
△ ST	5										0	9	
ST	14										0	9	
AE	16										20	16	
DEFICIT	0										-12	0	
SURPLUS	5										0	9	

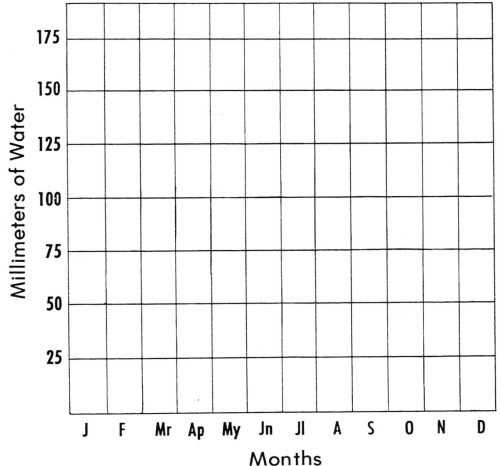

SURPLUS ⬤⬤⬤⬤⬤

STORAGE ═══

AE ----

P ▬▬▬

Millimeters of Water

J F Mr Ap My Jn Jl A S O N D

Months

Name _____ Date _____

NEW ORLEANS, LOUISIANA WATER BUDGET
water measured in millimeters

	JAN.	FEB.	MAR.	APR.	MAY	JUNE	JULY	AUG.	SEPT.	OCT.	NOV.	DEC.	TOTAL
P	127	133	142	134	119	115	136	106	73	85	111	152	1433
PE	15	18	45	75	122	164	179	170	129	69	31	15	1032
P-PE				59									
△ ST				0									
ST				100									
AE				75									
DEFICIT				0									
SURPLUS				59									

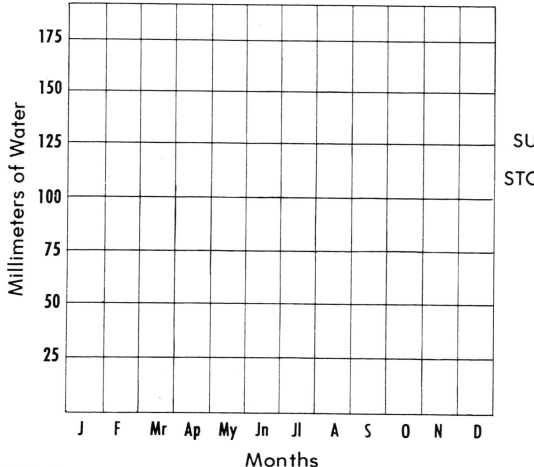

SURPLUS ⬚⬚⬚⬚⬚⬚⬚

STORAGE ═══════

AE ▬ ▬ ▬ ▬

P ━━━━━

Millimeters of Water

175
150
125
100
75
50
25

J   F   Mr   Ap   My   Jn   Jl   A   S   O   N   D

Months

MAPPING STREAM ORDER

Illustrate one of the major river systems in North America. Carry it to the highest order possible. Use different colored map pencils to indicate different orders.

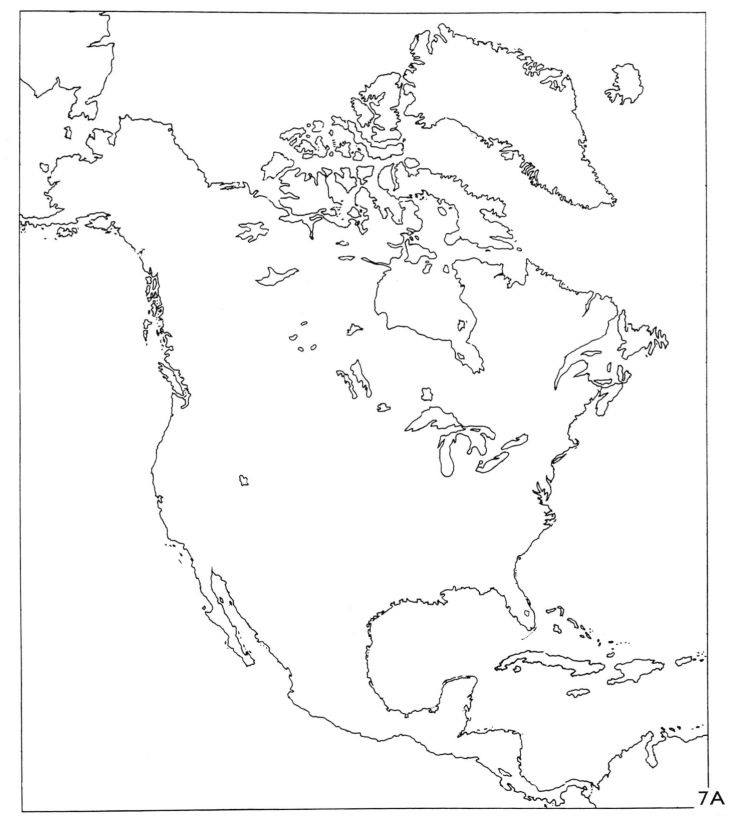

7A

MILLIKEN PUBLISHING CO.

LAKE SUCCESSION

Illustrate three stages of lake succession. Beside each stage, list four identifying characteristics.

1. _____

2. _____

3. _____

4. _____

1. _____

2. _____

3. _____

4. _____

1. _____

2. _____

3. _____

4. _____

8A

MILLIKEN PUBLISHING CO.

Name _____ Date _____

MAPPING OF GLACIERS AND ICECAPS

Name four centers of accumulation in which snow and ice were thickest during the

Ice Age: _____

Illustrate the extent to which ice from the continental centers covered land areas of North America.

1. Wisconsin

2. Illinoian

3. Kansan

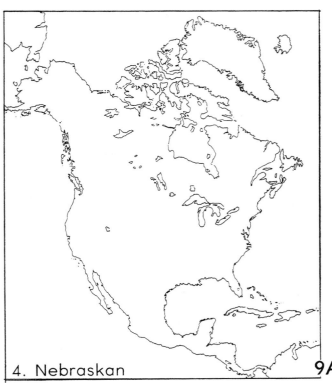

4. Nebraskan

9A

MILLIKEN PUBLISHING CO.

Name _____ Date _____

MAPPING THE OCEAN FLOORS

Draw a cross-section of the ocean floor from Seattle, Washington to Sidney, Australia (figure 1). Draw a cross section of the ocean floor from New York to Cape Town South Africa. (figure 2). Label physiographic features. Compare extent of continental shelf, numbers and locations of trenches, ridges, etc. Will this affect the amount and type of life in the two oceans? If so, which will support the most? Do you see any relationship between bottom features and ocean currents?

Figure 1.

Figure 2.

WATERS OF THE EARTH

MILLIKEN PUBLISHING CO.

Name _____ Date _____

MAPPING ANCIENT INLAND SEAS OF NORTH AMERICA I

On each of the following maps of North America, draw in and label the land and water areas for the Era or period mentioned. Also show any prominent features.

Precambrian Era

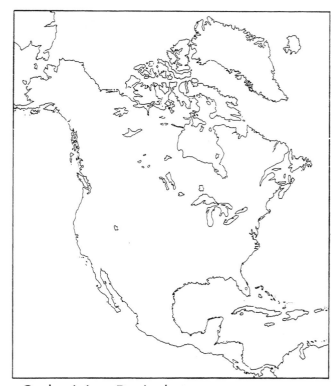

Ordovician Period

Silurian Period

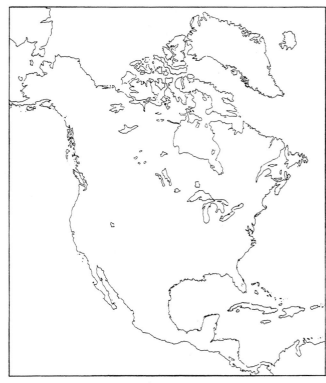

Devonian Period

WATERS OF THE EARTH

MILLIKEN PUBLISHING CO.

MAPPING ANCIENT INLAND SEAS OF NORTH AMERICA II

On each of the following maps of North America, draw in and label the land and water areas for the Era or period mentioned. Also show any prominent features.

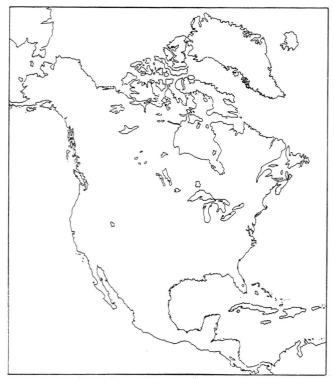

Pennsylvanian Period

Permian Period

Cretaceous Period

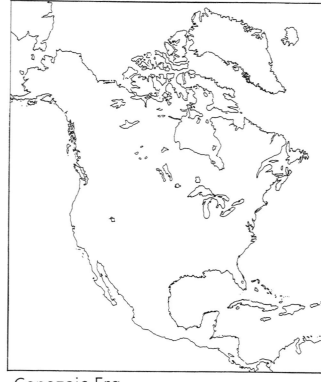

Cenozoic Era

11B

MILLIKEN PUBLISHING CO.

UNIT TEST FOR WATERS OF THE EARTH

A B C D 1. The combining volume ratio for the elements of which water is composed is
A. two volumes of oxygen to one of hydrogen.
B. two volumes of hydrogen to one of oxygen.
C. one volume hydrogen to one volume oxygen.
D. 1/2 volume oxygen to two volumes hydrogen.

A B C D 2. The formula of a hydrate must include
A. NaCl   C. H_2O
B. $CuSO_4$ D. NaOH

A B C D 3. Which of the following best describes the water molecule?
A. polar solvent
B. linear oxide
C. non-linear element
D. nonpolar hydrate

A B C D 4. Which of these processes does not involve water?
A. photosynthesis
B. crystallization
C. oxidation
D. hydration

A B C D 5. Water is colorless in small quantities. Why, then, do large bodies of water appear blue?
A. Blue algae live in large bodies of water.
B. They transmit short wave light.
C. Purifying agents turn water blue.
D. Colder temperature of large bodies make water blue.

A B C D 6. The weight of one milliliter of water taken at 4°C is the definition of
A. density.   C. specific gravity.
B. the gram. D. a calorie.

A B C D 7. The calibration indices for thermometers are
A. 0°C and 100°C
B. 100°C and 273°C.
C. 32°K and 273°K.
D. 212°F and 373°K.

A B C D 8. The amount of heat needed to raise one gram of water one degree Centigrade from 14.5°C to 15.5°C is called the
A. heat of fusion.
B. B.T.U.
C. heat of vaporization.
D. calorie.

A B C D 9. The heat needed to change one gram of ice at 0°C to one gram of water at 0°C is called
A. heat of fusion.
B. heat of condensation.
C. heat of vaporization.
D. a calorie.

A B C D 10. The number of calories needed to convert one gram of water at 100°C to one gram of steam at 100°C is
A. 84. B. 1. C. 540. D. 1000.

A B C D 11. Detergents make water "wetter" by
A. increasing capillarity.
B. decreasing temperature.
C. increasing cohesiveness.
D. weakening surface tension.

A B C D 12. Water has a maximum density at which temperature?
A. 0°C B. 4°C C. 100°C D. 32°C

A B C D 13. Which of these forms of water is noncrystalline?
A. ice   C. snow
B. steam   D. frost

A B C D 14. Crystalline water occupies a volume
A. 1/9 greater than noncrystalline water.
B. 1/9 less than noncrystalline water.
C. equal to that of noncrystalline water.
D. twice that of noncrystalline water.

A B C D 15. Accessible water accounts for what part of the earth's mass?
A. 99.9%   C. .024%
B. 50%   D. 25%

A B C D 16. The oceans contain about 97.2% of all the earth's water which is approximately
A. 319 billion cubic feet.
B. 317 million cubic miles.
C. 326 million cubic feet.
D. 327 billion cubic yards.

A B C D 17. Due to evaporation and density differences the oceans are saltiest in the
A. temperate area.
B. north polar area.
C. south polar area.
D. tropical area.

A B C D 18. Today glaciers contain what part of the earth's accessible water?
A. 50%   C. 4.37%
B. 2.15%   D. 90%

A B C D 19. The largest storehouse of ice is the glacier at
A. the north pole.
B. Alaska.
C. Iceland.
D. the Antarctic.

A B C D 20. Water-yielding strata in the earth's crust are called
A. wells.   C. glaciers.
B. aquifers.   D. hydrants.

A B C D 21. Water which has the shortest cycle, or is circulated most frequently is that of the
A. glaciers.   C. oceans.
B. ground water. D. atmosphere.

A B C D 22. Which of the following is not a contributing factor to the greater effectiveness of evaporation over land than over oceans?
A. Land has greater interface in proportion to depth.
B. Higher temperatures are reached over land.
C. There is more dry warm air over land.
D. Lower temperatures are reached over land.

A B C D 23. Which major precipitation pattern is significant where moisture-laden prevailing winds encounter mountain ranges?
A. orographic
B. cyclonic
C. convectional
D. air mass pattern

A B C D 24. A thunderstorm takes place somewhere in the world every 8 seconds. Which precipitation pattern is significant?
A. orographic   C. convectional
B. cyclonic   D. air mass

MILLIKEN PUBLISHING CO.

A B C D 25. The rain shadow is a
A. dry area on the windward side of the mountain.
B. wet area on the windward side of the mountain.
C. dry area on the leeward side of a mountain.
D. wet area on the leeward side of a mountain.

A B C D 26. The greatest percent of the precipitation that falls to the surface falls over the oceans. This precipitation forms the
A. null cycle.
B. short loop.
C. long loop.
D. infiltration process.

A B C D 27. What percent of precipitation that penetrates the ground gets as far as the water table and becomes ground water?
A. 10% B. 50% C. 80% D. 100%

A B C D 28. Approximately what amount of water is required per day by an individual for drinking purposes?
A. 1 liter   C. 3 gallons
B. 2 quarts   D. 5 pints

A B C D 29. For purposes of water budgeting, field capacity, or the soil's maximum storage capacity is usually considered to be
A. 400 inches.   C. 100 mm.
B. 6 mm.   D. 100 inches.

A B C D 30. Which of the following is not a region in the zone of aeration?
A. soil water region
B. intermediate region
C. capillary fringe region
D. annular region

A B C D 31. Most subsurface water is
A. meteoric.   C. connate.
B. magmatic. D. marine.

A B C D 32. Which soil type would hold most capillary water?
A. sandy   C. clay
B. loam   D. gravel

A B C D 33. Water that is trapped in the pores of sedimentary rock at the time it is laid down is
A. meteoric.   C. connate.
B. magmatic. D. marine.

A B C D 34. The downward migration of gravity water is called
A. condensation.
B. percolation.
C. infiltration.
D. capillarity.

A B C D 35. If the soil is at full field capacity and precipitation exceeds evapotranspiration, which is more likely to occur?
A. seepage   C. evaporation
B. runoff   D. transpiration

A B C D 36. Water movement in the zone of aeration is generally
A. vertical.   C. in arcs.
B. lateral.   D. very oblique.

A B C D 37. The depth of the soil water region is determined by
A. depth of capillary fringe region.
B. depth of weathered and organic material.
C. depth of the water table.
D. depth of the intermediate region.

A B C D 38. Layers on the zone of saturation that yield gravity water are called
A. springs.   C. aquifers.
B. aquicludes. D. wells.

15

A B C D 39. A geyser differs from a spring in that water from a geyser
    A. is ejected in an explosive manner above the aquifer.
    B. is ejected in an orderly manner on the level of the aquifer.
    C. is always hot while springs are always cold.
    D. contains no minerals similar to those in a spring.

A B C D 40. The path that runoff water follows is called a
    A. basin.   C. levee.
    B. watershed.   D. channel.

A B C D 41. A drainage pattern in which streams of the same order generally run parallel to each other and have tributaries which intercept them at nearly right angles is the
    A. dendritic.   C. radial.
    B. rectangular. D. trellis.

A B C D 42. A drainage channel with no tributaries is classified as a
    A. 1st order stream.
    B. 2nd order stream.
    C. 3rd order stream.
    D. 4th order stream.

A B C D 43. Based on the flow pattern of a stream there are three main types. Which of the following is not a flow pattern?
    A. permanent C. dendritic
    B. intermittent D. interrupted

A B C D 44. The chronological age of a lake is generally calculated by
    A. radiocarbon dating.
    B. counting varves.
    C. measuring size.
    D. observing its color.

A B C D 45. Lakes that are produced by the meandering of rivers are:
    A. tectonic.   C. solution.
    B. glacial.   D. oxbow.

A B C D 46. Lakes whose basins are formed by movement of the earth's crust are
    A. tectonic.   C. solution.
    B. glacial.   D. oxbow.

A B C D 47. The distinction between a lake and a pond is that
    A. ponds have salt water, while lakes are fresh water.
    B. ponds usually have rooted plants growing from one side to the other.
    C. lakes usually support woody stemmed plants.
    D. lakes are always at least 500 ft. deep, while ponds are shallow.

A B C D 48. The deepest known lake is
    A. Lake Erie.
    B. Lake Baikal.
    C. Crater Lake.
    D. Reelfoot Lake.

A B C D 49. Bodies of water which continuously shrink in size with age are:
    A. rivers.   C. oceans.
    B. lakes.   D. streams.

A B C D 50. The usual sequence of stages in the life of a lake is
    A. oligotrophic   eutrophic   marsh   swamp.
    B. oligotrophic   marsh   eutrophic   swamp.
    C. swamp   marsh   eutrophic   oligotrophic.
    D. marsh   oligotrophic   swamp   eutrophic.

16